Negative Thoughts Don't = **A *POSITIVE* LIFE**

A Journal for Reflecting, Inspiring
&
Self-Exploration

Maria Shkreli, LMHC

First Series: March 2022

Printed in the United States of America.

ISBN-13: 9780578378794

To my Mom and Dad:

I love you unconditionally.

Thank you!

Introduction

In a changing world, it is not always easy to navigate. These challenges and obstacles are part of one's growth to evolve into a healthy authentic self.

I am excited for you as you embark on a journey of reflection, inspiration, and self-exploration. With this keepsake journal, you bring reflection into each page as you find your authentic self through your own work and time.

I hope you make this a great trip and develop a better relationship with yourself.

Maria Shkreli is a licensed Mental Health Therapist and author practicing in Pleasantville, NY. (therapy4growth.com) Her specialties include working with Anxiety, ADHD, Family Conflict, Couple Conflict, Toxic Relationships, and Personality Diagnoses. Additionally, she is the author of My 14-Day Anxiety Challenge, Colorful Emotion, Help! My Anxious Middle Schooler, The DSM-5 MisUNDERSTOOD, The Simplified NCMHCE Study Guide, and the College Student's Guide to Understanding the DSM—5.

This

Journal

Belongs to:

_____

Who are you when no one is around?

What is on your bucket list? Don't have one? Now it's time to make one.

What about your upbringing are you grateful for?

Date: _____

Write a poem about a time you got lost and made an adventure out of it.

> *"Add a positive word to your day that starts with the first letter of your name."*
> *--Unknown*

Your word:

_____

Date: _____

How have your values changed from ten years ago?

Date: _____

What is the last compliment you received? How did it make you feel?

Date: _____

What truths about yourself do you prefer to ignore?

Have you ever been lonely? How did you feel?

*"Mistakes are a fact
of life. It is the
response to the errors
that counts."*
--Nikki Giovanni

Act of kindness:

Send a card to someone you haven't spoken to in a while.

We all make mistakes in life, but that doesn't mean you have to pay for them for the rest of your life. It means you are human. What mistakes have you made?

Date: _____

Why or how are you a better person today than you were yesterday?

Date: _____

Go back to a time when you were hurt. Write a letter to the person who hurt you, explaining to them how they hurt you. At the end, forgive them.

Dear _____,

Date: _____

What behaviors bother you about other other people? Why?

"If you continue to think the way you've always thought, you'll continue to get what you've always got."
--Kevin Trudeau

Date: _____

How have you controlled the direction of your life this year?

Date: _____

Write 3 things you are grateful for today:

What lessons did you learn in the last year that changed your life?

Look through old pictures. Write about how you felt at the time, or how you feel now looking at the old pictures.

"We aren't given a good life or a bad life. We are given a life. It's up to us to make it good or bad."

--Unknown

Date: _____

Write a letter to your future self, describing your life story.

Date: _____

What life experience(s) have taught you the most about life?

Write the top 8 things in your life that cause you stress. For each stress factor, write what you can do to change it.

Make a list of 15 ways you are fortunate.

"The 3 C's of life: Choices, Chances, Changes. You must make the choice, to take a chance, if you want anything in life to change."
--Zig Ziglar

Act of kindness:

Send a positive text message to six different people right now.

Date: _____

"Stop shrinking to fit into places you've outgrown." *--Unknown*

Reflect on this quote:

Are you living in the past? How?

What material items are you grateful for?

Date: _____

If you can only keep 5 things you have, what would they be and why?

"When a negative thought enters your mind, think three positive ones. Train yourself to flip the script."
--Unknown

My positive word for this week:

_____

What song describes your life? Why?

Date: _____

Your own thoughts:

How good do you consider your mental health to be?

Date: _____

How would you describe yourself to a stranger?

Date: _____

Do you see yourself as an extrovert, introvert, or ambivert? Why?

"Never give up, because great things take time."
--Curiano

Act of kindness:

Write a kind message on your mirror for yourself, your partner, or a family member.

Date: _____

What are you currently worried about?

Date: _____

Write a letter to your mom.

Dear Mom,

Because of you, I am who I am today..

Date: _____

Check-in. Since starting this journal, are you feeling more connected with yourself?

"The future belongs to those who believe in the beauty of their dreams."

--*Eleanor Roosevelt*

Date: _____

What is something you're grateful to have learned or done this week?

Are you truly living or just existing?

Do you think there is really any selfless act of kindness, or are there motives behind helping others?

Date: _____

Tomorrow night, step outside and look at the moon and stars.

Write about how you feel.

> *"Note to self: Small steps in the right direction are better than big steps in the wrong direction."*
>
> *--Unknown*

Act of kindness:

Leave a good server a bigger tip.

Date: _____

What song describes your personality?

Date: _____

Pick a random photo and write about that memory.

Date: _____

List all your favorite songs:

Date: _____

Tomorrow I look forward to:

"You can't always choose
what happens to you, but
you can always choose
how you feel about it."
--Danielle Laporte

Date: _____

What I want to remember about today:

Date: _____'

This week, drive by a childhood setting you haven't been to in a long time that you have fond memories about. Write about it.

Date: _____

Take a moment and find a mirror. Look into the mirror and write about what you see and what you feel.

Date: _____

What do you need to forgive yourself for?

"Don't be a victim of your negative thoughts."
--Unknown

Act of kindness:

Leave a sticky note with a positive note somewhere in public.

Date: _____

What do you value the most about yourself?

Date: _____

Do you consider yourself non-judgmental? Are you open-minded? Do you seek to understand others before jumping to conclusions?

Date: _____

Think of the people you feel judged by. Write down why their opinions of you are wrong.

Date: _____

Who are the people who believe in you?

"6 + 3= 9 but so does 5+4.
The way you do things isn't
always the only way to do
them. Respect other
people's way of thinking."
--Unknown

My positive word for this week:

_____

Date: _____

Where do your high expectations of yourself stem from?

What's your philosophy of life?

Date: _____

Your thoughts:

Date: _____

If I continue doing what I've been doing every day, where will I be in one year?

Date: _____

Write a letter to your dad.

Dear Dad,

Because of you, I am who I am today..

> *"Not all storms come to disrupt your life. Some come to clear your path."*
> *--Unknown*

Act of kindness:

Tell someone you love them.

Date: _____

Watch an old home video. Write about the experience.

Date: _____

What book had the most significant impact on your life?

Date: _____

What is keeping you from changing the things you'd like to change about yourself?

"Whenever I hear someone sigh, 'Life is hard,' I'm always tempted to ask, 'Compared to what?'"
--Sydney Harris

Act of kindness:

Hug someone today.

Date: _____

Buy yourself a new book. Why did you buy this particular book?

Date: _____

If you didn't have to work to make money, how would you spend your time?
What would you do, or create?

Make a list of 5 of your positive personality traits.

Make a list of 5 of your negative personality traits.

"Don't be pushed by your problems. Be led by your dreams."

--Ralph Waldo Emerson

Act of kindness:

Buy someone's coffee this week.

Date: _____

When do you seek distractions? What are your distractions?

Date: _____

What would you do differently if you knew no one would judge you?

Are you holding onto something you need to let go of?

Date: _____

What negative experiences seem to repeat in your life?

*"You are the
greatest project you
will ever work on."*
--Unknown

My positive word for this week:

_____

Write a thank-you letter to someone.

What do you take for granted?

Date: _____

Expectations are the strong belief that something will happen or should be a certain way. More than anything else, our **expectations** determine our reality, and our **expectations** also impact those around us. In a self-fulfilling prophecy, people may rise or fall depending on our **expectations** and beliefs.

What are your expectations?

Date: _____

Your own thoughts:

Date: _____

Are you a good example for those around you?

"Don't be afraid to change. You may lose something good, and you may gain something better."
--Unknown

Act of kindness:

Donate old clothes you do not need.

Date: _____

What are your hobbies?

How can you start your mornings more mindfully?

Date: _____

If you could live anywhere in the world, where would you live?

What is your wildest fantasy?

"I can't always control my thoughts, but I can choose how I respond to them."
--David Cuschieri

My positive word for this week:

_____

"You can either be judged because you created something or or ignored because you left your greatness inside of you." --James Clear

Reflect on this quote. What does it mean to you?

Date: _____

What does success mean to you?

Date: _____

What is something you have always wanted to try, but never have?

Date: _____

Who do you compare yourself to? How does it make you feel?

"There is only one thing that makes a dream impossible to achieve: the fear of failure."
--Paulo Coelho

Act of kindness:

Tell a friend what you love about them.

If you could pick a superpower, what would it be? Why?

Date: _____

What is your favorite season? Why?

"I expect nothing and accept everything."

What does this mean to you?

Date: _____

How would you describe the relationship between your parents? Does it influence your view on love and marriage?

*"Life is a one-time offer.
Live it well."*
--Unknown

Date: _____

Write a letter to your past self. What would you want to say?

Date: _____

In what scenario, if any, is it okay to lie?

It's a conscious choice of how we want to live and how we want to be seen. Think of yourself and define what authenticity means to you. Ask yourself, "Who am I supposed to be, and who am I?"

Date: _____

How do you communicate your feelings?

"Reset.
Restart.
Refocus.
As many times as you need to."
--Steve Maraboli

My positive word for this week:

_____

What lies do you most often tell yourself?

Which is worse: failing or never trying?

Date: _____

What quality served as a strenght in the past but is now a weeakness for you?

Date: _____

Who is the person you hurt the most?

"The greatest weapon against stress is our ability to choose one thought over another."
--William James

Date: _____

Make a list of 20 things that make you smile:

Date: _____

Take a walk and listen to a motivational podcast. What did you learn?

Date: _____

What matters most in your life?

Date: _____

When setting goals, are you **Interested** (you come up with excuses for why you can't do these goals) or are you **Committed** (you do whatever it takes to meet these goals)? Which are you?

*"If you want change,
focus on changing
yourself, not others."*
--Unknown

My positive word for this week:

_____

Date: _____

Your own thoughts:

Write a thank-you letter to yourself.

Date: _____

List 5 compliments you can give to others:

Date: _____

What is the best gift you received? Write about how you felt.

What is your biggest insecurity?

"Stop being afraid of what could go wrong and think of what could go right."
--*Unknown*

Act of kindness:

Put your phone away when in the company of others.

Date: _____

What go-to coping strategies help you get through moments of emotional pain?

Who is your best friend? Write about the most amazing time you had with this person and why it means so much to you.

Date: _____

Make a list of everything you'd like to say no to:

You live life every day as you know it, and one day life will come to an end. How would you respond to the following: I gave you all these opportunities to live your best life, pursue your dreams, find your true happiness, and noticed you didn't follow through on many opportunities - what happened?

How would you answer this question?

"Remember, you can't reach what's in front of you until you let go of what's behind you."
--Unknown

Date: _____

How do you handle anger and frustration?

Date: _____

Cut words and/or photos out of newspapers or magazines and make a collage. Write about your collage.

Date: _____

What are ten things that are really important to you?

What three things are you most proud of in your life so far?

*"Do not learn how to react.
Learn how to respond!"*
--Buddha

My positive word for this week:

_____

Date: _____

I really wish others knew this about me:

Date: _____

Being myself is hard because . . .

Make a list of everything you'd like to say yes to:

Date: _____

Have you done anything lately that's worth remembering?

"Train your mind to see the good in every situation."
--Unknown

Date: _____

If you had the opportunity, what would you tell your childhood self?

Date: _____

What battles have you fought and overcome in your life?

Date: _____

What are you going to do today to be happier moving forward?

Date: _____

Are you flexible with your thinking or are you rigid? Write down what you are not flexible with. As you read it over, decide if you can move it to the "flexible side." Reflect on what is left on the rigid thoughts side.

Rigid thoughts   Can be flexible with

*"Look for something positive
each day, even if some days you
have to look a little harder."*

Date: _____

What is something you wish you did this year but didn't because you were afraid?

Date: _____

If you had more time to do what you love, what would you do?

Date: _____

How have you stepped out of your comfort zone this month?

What are four things you admire about three people in your life?

"No one ever injured their eyesight by looking on the bright side."
--Unknown

My positive word for this week:

_____

Date: _____

Write a letter to someone who believed in you when you didn't believe it in yourself.

Date: _____

What do you like about your generation?

Date: _____

When telling your grandchildren about your life, what would you like to say?

*"Every day is a chance
to be better."*
--Unknown

Date: _____

How old are you? How does it feel to be the age you are?

Date: _____

Negative core beliefs are beliefs (assumptions/expectations) we think about ourselves (our identity), others, and the world. These beliefs are also our security, insecurity, self-doubt, and validation of ourselves. They are also assumptions that influence our behavior, how we see others, and situations.

What are your negative core beliefs?

Date: _____

What boundaries do you need to set with others and yourself for self care?

Date: _____

I am going to make my life about ....

"The way we see the problem is the problem."

--Stephen Covey

Date: _____

Choose six photos of yourself across your lifetime and reflect. Write about you, and what you were like in those photos.

Photo page

Photo page

"A positive mind looks for ways it can done; A negative mind looks for ways it can't be done."
--Napoleon Hill

My positive word for this week:

_____

Date: _____

Every month for the next six months, you are going to do something different. You are going to do something new: get out of your rut, say yes to something you would normally say no to, start a hobby, get a different haircut, wear different clothing, try a new activity. It can be anything, and you are going to do it. Write about all these new experiences here.

"Don't wait for things to get better. Life will always be complicated. Learn how to be happy right now, otherwise, you'll run out of time."
--Unknown

What comes to your mind when you read this quote?

If you were gratitude, how would you express yourself in a way that is meaningful?

Date: _____

Take time to reflect. How have you changed in the past 5 years? What have you learned?

Date: _____

Where do you see yourself in 5 years?

"When one door of happiness closes, another opens, but often we look so long at the closed door that we do not see the one that has been opened for us."
--Helen Keller

Act of kindness:

Hide money in a random place for a stranger to find.

What makes you feel optimistic?

Date: _____

Who are the five closest people in your life? Describe your relationship with each of these people.

Date: _____

In what area are you lacking confidence?

"Our attitude towards life determines life's attitude towards us."
--John Mitchell

Date: _____

How can you improve your self-confidence?

Date: _____

What do you hope to move on from in the future?

Sometimes we are bothered by outside noise - people telling us what to do, judging us and our opinions. How do you minimize the outside noise?

Do you seek external validation (parents, friends, social media) to feel complete?

Date: _____

A person can fall in love at least three times in their lifetime. The first love is the idealistic fairytale love. The second love is the intense one that teaches us lessons about who we are and how we want to be loved. The third is unconditional love, the love that can't be explained and connects you with the person who accepts you and you accept them. Write about your love experiences.

"Well done is better than well said."

--Benjamin Franklin

List four personal beliefs that you are willing to reconsider. Explain why.

Start a time capsule. Share its meaning for you.

Does silence make you uncomfortable? Why?

*"Don't let anyone
dull your sparkle."*
--Unknown

Act of kindness:

Compliment someone on their work.

Date: _____

What bad habit(s) do you have? What are you going to do to change this habit?
You can start now and change this habit for the next fourteen days.

Am I moral or ethical?

Date: _____

Who are you right now? Describe yourself.

Do you want to live forever? Why or why not?

Date: _____

Write down any accomplishments you've made from your bucket list.

Date: _____

Write down six positive affirmations that you can recite when you are overwhelmed, frustrated, angry, and/or disappointed.

Where do you see yourself in 10 years?

Do you like who you have become?

Date: _____

Write a letter to your future self, asking for guidance and everything else you need on the way to becoming the best version of yourself.

Dear _____,

Date: _____

"Never get so
Busy
Making a living
That You
Forget to
Make a
LIFE"
--anonymous

Reflect on this quote. What does it mean to you?

Date: _____

Your own thoughts:

"Keep looking

up...that's the secret of life."

--Charlie Brown

63550151R00109